AN ARK
AND A RAINBOW

AN ARK
AND A RAINBOW

Noah and the Ark for Beginning Readers

Genesis 6—9 FOR CHILDREN

by Sibyl Hancock
illustrated by Aline Cunningham

I CAN READ A BIBLE STORY
Series Editor: Dorothy Van Woerkom

Publishing House
St. Louis

FOR MY SON, KEVIN

Concordia Publishing House, St. Louis, Missouri
Copyright © 1976 Concordia Publishing House

Manufactured in the United States of America

Library of Congress Cataloging in Publication Data

Hancock, Sibyl.
    An ark and a rainbow.

    (I can read a Bible story)
    SUMMARY: Easy-to-read retelling of the story of Noah and the ark
he built to withstand a flood which covered the earth.
    1. Noah's ark—Juvenile literature. 2. Deluge—Juvenile literature. [1.
Noah's ark. 2. Bible stories—O. T.] I. Cunningham, Aline. II. Title.
BS658.H25   222′.11′09505   76-14924
ISBN 0-570-07309-X
ISBN 0-570-07303-0 pbk.

Noah

lived long ago,

when the earth was young.

He was a good man.

He loved God

and was faithful to Him.

Noah and his wife

had three sons who were named

Shem, Ham, and Japheth.

The people who lived on the earth
were mean and selfish.
They did not love God.
Noah and his family were sad
to see so many bad people.
God was sad, too.
But more than that, He was angry.

"I made people to look like me,"
God said.

"I gave them love.

But these people only

hate each other."

But God knew that Noah

was good and kind.

God told Noah,

"Soon I will send a flood

to cover the earth.

Every living thing will die.

But if you do as I tell you,

you and your family

will be saved.

You must build an ark."

Noah listened

as God told him how to

build the great ark.

Then Noah said to his sons,
"We will cut down trees
to make wood."

For many days,
Noah and his family worked.
They built the ark.
They made a roof for it.
They put a door in the side.

"Melt some tar," Noah said,

"And paint the ark with it."

The tar was black and sticky.

It would keep the water out.

At last the ark was finished.

It was three stories high.

It had many rooms.

"It's a fine ark," Ham said.

"But what is it for?"

"It's much too big for us,"
Japheth said.

God spoke again to Noah.

"Soon the flood will come.

All of the people

and all of their evil

will be washed away.

It will rain for forty days

and for forty nights."

God told Noah to find two

of every creature

that lived on the earth.

First Noah made large pens

for the creatures.

They would be safe there

until it was time to go

into the ark.

Then they all went to look
for the animals.
They brought back two tiny ants
and two great elephants.

Two of every kind of bird that sang.
Two mice. Two rats.
Two goats. Two sheep.

"They are all here," Shem said at last.

"We have two of every kind of

living creature

we could find."

"We have done well," Noah said.

"Now we can rest."

After the ark was built,

people came to see it.

Noah told them about the flood

that God was going to send.

"Hah!" they laughed.

"The old man is crazy!"

They laughed, but

the earth began to change.

The sky grew dark,

and the wind blew through the trees.

The sun grew dim.

It was only noontime,

but the day was dark as night.

The creatures were

frightened.

The birds stopped singing.

Everything was very still and quiet.

God called to Noah.

The time had come

to go into the ark.

"Come," Noah said.

"We must hurry."

"I am frightened," Ham said.

"So are we all," Noah told him.

Two by two

the animals were led into the ark.

"Make the creatures hurry,"

Japheth said.

"We may not finish in time!"

Noah looked at the dark sky.
There was a strange yellow light
all around.
The wind blew sand and dust
about in the air.
Lightning flashed in the sky.
God shut the door of the ark.

Thunder boomed,

and the earth shook.

"Listen!" Noah cried.

"It's beginning to rain!"

It rained a little.

Then it rained a lot.

The earth opened up,

and water came

out of the cracks.

"I have never heard such rain,"
Noah's wife said.

Water rushed around the ark
and lifted it from the ground.

The ark was floating!

The water grew deeper
and deeper.

"Let's see if the creatures

are safe," Noah said.

Each one went a different way.

They took clay lamps

filled with oil

to light their way.

The large bins of food and grain
were dry.

The animals were safe.

All was well.

It rained for forty days
and forty nights.

Noah and his family cared for
the animals and listened to the rain.

But one day the rain stopped.

All was quiet.

The sky was still dark.

Was it day or was it night?

No one knew.

Shem stood at the window.

The others were asleep.

It was his turn to

watch the ark.

Suddenly Shem cried, "Oh!"

Through the darkness

he saw the golden rim of a cloud.

The sun was rising!

"Wake up!" he shouted.

"Come quickly."

The others hurried
to the window.
"It's the sun!" Noah said.
They all kneeled down
to thank God
for bringing the sun back
again.

The birds began to sing.

The animals tried to leave
their pens.

But there was no land yet.

A warm wind blew across the water.

And the water began to go down.

One day Noah saw the top of a
mountain
rising out of the water.
"Bring me a raven," he said.
Noah let the raven fly
through the window.
The raven did not return.
It found food
on top of the water.
It did not need the ark any more.

Noah waited seven days.

"Bring me a dove," he said.

The dove was gentle.

She would return to the ark if there

was no land for her to rest on.

Noah turned her loose.

She soon flew back to the ark.

After seven more days,

Noah let the dove fly again.

She came back with an olive leaf

in her bill.

"The water is going down,"

Noah said.

Seven more days passed.

Noah let the dove fly

one more time.

The dove did not return.

Then God told Noah to
leave the ark.
Noah and his family took the roof
off the ark.
They stood in the warm sunlight.

Then they opened the door.

The door made a wooden bridge

for the animals.

Noah and his family led the

creatures of the earth

onto the dry land.

The air smelled sweet

and felt cool.

Noah built an altar to God,

and God blessed him.

They all prayed,

and a mist came into the sky.

It made an arch

of many beautiful colors.

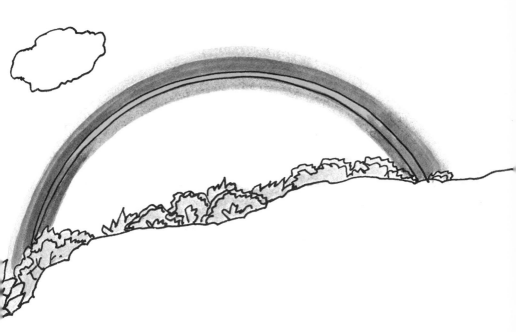

"This is a rainbow,"

God told Noah.

"It's a sign of My promise

never again to flood the earth."

Noah and his family

were filled with joy.

The earth was theirs once more.

ABOUT THE AUTHOR

Sibyl Hancock has contributed articles and stories to magazines and newspapers, and is the author of *Mosshaven,* a novel for adults. Her main hobby is collecting old children's books, which eventually led her into writing for children. Two of her children's books are for beginning readers: *Mario's Mystery Machine* and *The Blazing Hills.* She has also written *The Grizzly Bear* for middle readers, and is co-author and co-artist of the word-picture book *Let's Learn Hawaiian.* Ms. Hancock is also an amateur astronomer and has her own telescope. She lives in Houston with her husband and young son.

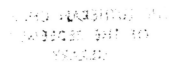